Reflections on a Gift of Watermelon Pickle...

AND OTHER MODERN VERSE

compiled by

STEPHEN DUNNING

EDWARD LUEDERS

HUGH SMITH

Reflections on a Gift of Watermelon Pickle...

AND OTHER MODERN VERSE

STEPHEN DUNNING

EDWARD LUEDERS

HUGH SMITH

Editorial direction: LEO B. KNEER

Development: NORA ROTZOLL
Elizabeth Waud, Harold Eaton

Design: DONALD MARVINE

SCOTT, FORESMAN AND COMPANY

PHOTOGRAPH CREDITS

ACKNOWLEDGMENTS

"Absolutes" by Gustave Keyser, from *New Mexico Quarterly* (Autumn 1963). © 1963 by the University of New Mexico Press. "Advice to Travelers" from COME AS YOU ARE, © 1958 by Walker Gibson, reprinted by permission of Hastings House, Publishers, Inc. Originally appeared in *Saturday Review*. "African Sunrise" by Gertrude May Lutz, from *Contemporary Poetry* (Winter 1944). Reprinted by permission of the author. "Ancient History" from the book LYRIC LAUGHTER by Arthur Guiterman. Copyright, 1939, by E. P. Dutton & Co., Inc. Reprinted by permission of the publishers. "Angler's Choice" by H. J. Gottlieb on page 105, reprinted by permission, copyright © 1955 The New Yorker Magazine, Inc. "Apartment House" by Gerald Raftery from *The New York Sun*. Reprinted by permission of Communications Advisors, Inc. "April" by Marcia Lee Masters, from *Contemporary Poetry* (Winter 1944). Reprinted by permission of the author. "April" from COLLECTED POEMS by Yvor Winters, by permission of the publishers, Alan Swallow and Routledge & Kegan Paul, Ltd. Copyright 1952, 1960, by Yvor Winters. "Arithmetic" from COMPLETE POEMS, copyright, 1950, by Carl Sandburg. Reprinted by permission of Harcourt, Brace & World, Inc. "August from My Desk" by Roland Flint, from *The Atlantic Monthly* (February 1965). Copyright © 1965, by The Atlantic Monthly Company, Boston, Massachusetts 02116. Reprinted with permission.

"The Base Stealer." Copyright 1948 by Robert Francis. Reprinted from THE ORB WEAVER by Robert Francis, by permission of Wesleyan University Press. "The Bat" by Ruth Herschberger, from *Poetry Magazine* (April 1951). Reprinted by permission of the author. "The Bat." Copyright 1938 by Theodore Roethke, from the book, WORDS FOR THE WIND by Theodore Roethke. Reprinted by permission of Doubleday & Company, Inc., and Mrs. Theodore Roethke. "Bones" from STUFF AND NONSENSE by Walter de la Mare. Reprinted by permission of The Society of Authors, representatives of The Literary Trustees of Walter de la Mare. "Boy with Frogs" by Sy Kahn from OUR SEPARATE DARKNESS. Reprinted by permission of the author. "The Builders," copyright © 1961 by Sara Henderson Hay. Originally appeared in the *Saturday Review*. From the book THE STORY HOUR by Sara Henderson Hay. Reprinted by permission of Doubleday & Company, Inc.

"Carmel Point" by Margaret Phyllis MacSweeney. Copyright 1930 by Scholastic Magazines, Inc. "Catalogue" by Rosalie Moore on page 89, reprinted by permission, copyright 1940 The New Yorker Magazine, Inc. "Central Park Tourney" by Mildred Weston on page 47, reprinted by permission, copyright 1953 The New Yorker Magazine, Inc. "Cheers." Copyright © 1964 by Eve Merriam. From IT DOESN'T ALWAYS HAVE TO RHYME. Used by Permission of Atheneum Publishers. "Child on Top of a Greenhouse" by Theodore Roethke, copyright 1946 by Editorial Publications, Inc. From the book, WORDS FOR THE WIND by Theodore Roethke. Reprinted by permission of Doubleday & Company, Inc., and Mrs. Theodore Roethke. "The Child's Morning." Appeared in *Saturday Review*. Copyright © 1963 by Winfield Townley Scott, from CHANGE OF WEATHER. Reprinted by permission of Doubleday & Company, Inc. "A Coney Island

Table
of
Contents

Note

In four years we found twelve hundred poems good enough to consider for *REFLECTIONS ON A GIFT OF WATERMELON PICKLE . . . AND OTHER MODERN VERSE*. Nine hundred of these we discarded after many readings. We tried out the remaining three hundred on each other, on students, and on the publisher. We argued about all of them. Over half of the poems in this book are those that students chose from those we thought were good enough. Here are four ideas that will help you read them:

1. Take your time in judging each poem. Poems don't spring from poets' brains. Poets spend more hours finding right words than you will spend minutes reading them. If a word or a line confuses you at first, try to discover why the poet may have left it just as he did.

2. Read each poem slowly. Give every poem a chance to speak to you. Reread. Read aloud. Make your ears and your eyes work on each poem. Expect to find surprises—then read slowly enough to enjoy them.

3. Read only a few poems at one time. The language of poetry is condensed. You will have to supply words that are missing and puzzle over lines that aren't clear at first reading. Better to read one or two poems well than to read a dozen poems carelessly.

4. Judge poems by their quality not by their subjects. You may not like cats, but there are good cat poems. You may not like (or even believe in) flying saucers, but whether you do or don't has no bearing on the quality of "Southbound on the Freeway" (page 82). You may like plain talk better than wild talk, but that has nothing to do with how well or how badly the poets talk in "Poets Hitchhiking on the Highway" (page 19). Read each poem with the idea that you will "let" the poet write on any subject he chooses and in any way he chooses.

Perhaps the best advice of all is in the following poem:

How to Eat a Poem

by Eve Merriam

Don't be polite.
Bite in.
Pick it up with your fingers and lick the juice that
    may run down your chin.
It is ready and ripe now, whenever you are.

You do ,not need a knife or fork or spoon
or plate or napkin or tablecloth.

For there is no core
or stem
or rind
or pit
or seed
or skin
to throw away.

Unfolding Bud

One is amazed
By a water-lily bud
Unfolding
With each passing day,
Taking on a richer color
And new dimensions.

One is not amazed,
At a first glance,
By a poem,
Which is as tight-closed
As a tiny bud.

Yet one is surprised
To see the poem
Gradually unfolding,
Revealing its rich inner self,
As one reads it
Again
And over again.

Naoshi Koriyama

Gone Forever

Halfway through shaving, it came—
the word for a poem.
I should have scribbled it
on the mirror with a soapy finger,
or shouted it to my wife in the kitchen,
or muttered it to myself till it ran
in my head like a tune.

But now it's gone with the whiskers
down the drain. Gone forever,
like the girls I never kissed,
and the places I never visited—
the lost lives I never lived.

Barriss Mills

Poets
    Hitchhiking
        on the
            Highway

Of course I tried to tell him
but he cranked his head
    without an excuse.
I told him the sky chases
    the sun
And he smiled and said:
    "What's the use."
I was feeling like a demon
    again
So I said: "But the ocean chases
    the fish."
This time he laughed
    and said: "Suppose the
        strawberry were
            pushed into a mountain."
After that I knew the
    war was on—
So we fought:
He said: "The apple-cart like a
        broomstick-angel
    snaps & splinters
        old dutch shoes."
I said: "Lightning will strike the old oak
    and free the fumes!"
He said: "Mad street with no name."
I said: "Bald killer! Bald killer! Bald killer!"
He said, getting real mad,
    "Firestoves! Gas! Couch!"
I said, only smiling,
    "I know God would turn back his head
    if I sat quietly and thought."
We ended by melting away,
    hating the air!

Gregory Corso

To Look

at

Any Thing

To look at any thing,
If you would know that thing,
You must look at it long:
To look at this green and say
'I have seen spring in these
Woods,' will not do—you must
Be the thing you see:
You must be the dark snakes of
Stems and ferny plumes of leaves,
You must enter in
To the small silences between
The leaves,
You must take your time
And touch the very peace
They issue from.

John Moffitt

SECTION TWO

Absolutes

(From an ink painting by Seiho)

black on white
crow in snow
      hunched
      wet lump
on brittle branch
remembering warmth
remembering corn
miserable
as life
is
black on white

        Gustave Keyser

The Crows   By Leah Bodine Drake

I shortcut home between Wade's tipsy shocks,
And lookout crows alert in the bare elm
Ask each other about this form that walks
Stubbled mud they considered their own farm.
They know there's death and loss where such shapes go.
I have no gun—I even feel akin
To these rude, lively birds. But to a crow
Kinship means Crow, and I'm not of his clan.

Off they flap to the wood with a hoarse curse,
And though the landscape's greyer with them gone
I'm glad they're skeptics—someday someone else
Trudging these ruts may raise a sudden gun.
Distrust me, crow!—the not-as-crow-, the other.
Croak, 'Damn your eyes!', and call no man your brother.

Crows

I like to walk
And hear the black crows talk.

I like to lie
And watch crows sail the sky.

I like the crow
That wants the wind to blow:

I like the one
That thinks the wind is fun.

I like to see
Crows spilling from a tree,

And try to find
The top crow left behind.

I like to hear
Crows caw that spring is near.

I like the great
Wild clamor of crow hate

Three farms away
When owls are out by day.

I like the slow
Tired homeward-flying crow;

I like the sight
Of crows for my good night.

David McCord

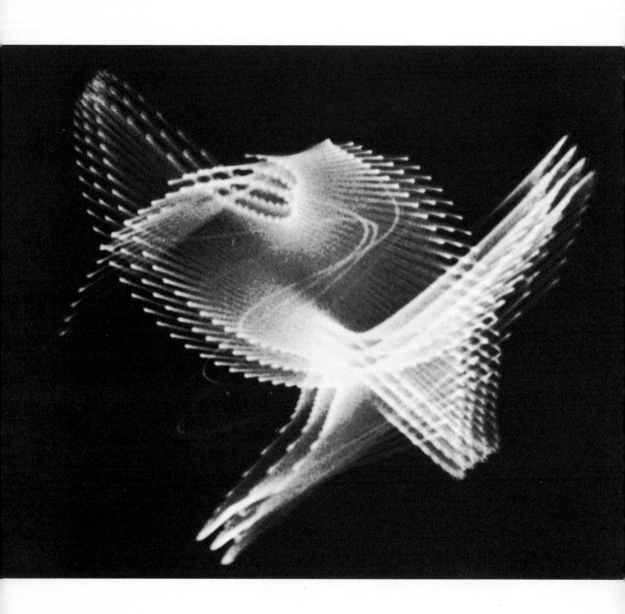

Some Brown Sparrows

Some brown sparrows who live
in the Bronx Zoo visit often
the captive Victoria Crested
Pheasant, visit captive Peacocks,
Cockatoos. They fly through bars
to visit also monkeys, jackals,
bears. They delouse themselves in
cage dust, shaking joyously;
they hunt for bread crumbs, seeds
or other tidbits. Briefly,
they lead free sparrow lives
and fly free.

Bruce Fearing

Swallows

The prairie wind blew harder than it could,
Even the spines of cactus trembled back,
I crouched in an arroyo clamping my hands
On my eyes the sand was stinging yellow black.

In a break of the black I let my lashes part,
Looked overhead and saw I was not alone,
I could almost reach through the roar and almost touch
A treadmill of swallows almost holding their own.

Thomas Hornsby Ferril

Seal

See how he dives
From the rocks with a zoom!
See how he darts
Through his watery room
Past crabs and eels
And green seaweed,
Past fluffs of sandy
Minnow feed!
See how he swims
With a swerve and a twist,
A flip of the flipper,
A flick of the wrist!
Quicksilver-quick,
Softer than spray,
Down he plunges
And sweeps away;
Before you can think,
Before you can utter
Words like "Dill pickle"
Or "Apple butter,"
Back up he swims
Past sting-ray and shark,
Out with a zoom,
A whoop, a bark;
Before you can say
Whatever you wish,
He plops at your side
With a mouthful of fish!

William Jay Smith

Boy with Frogs

Under his relentless eye,
Jarred and jeered,
The small frogs hop
And pulse in their
Suddenly glass world.

He, blond and curious,
Captive and captivated,
Holds in his hands
World of water, pebbles, grass
And the power
Of topsy-turvy and crash.

But he is content
To study them a while,
With their delicate legs
Pressed against the glass,
The futile leaps to freedom
And their frantic eyes.

It's a game for a God
Of course.
Later, the vibrant frogs,
Still leaping with protest
And life, are forgotten
On a shelf. He is out
Wondering about the waterbugs.

Sy Kahn

Giraffes

Stilted creatures,
Features fashioned as a joke,
Boned and buckled,
Finger painted,

They stand in the field
On long-pronged legs
As if thrust there.
They airily feed,
Slightly swaying,
Like hammer-headed flowers.

Bizarre they are,
Built silent and high,
Ornaments against the sky.
Ears like leaves
To hear the silken
Brushing of the clouds.

Sy Kahn

Why Nobody Pets the Lion at the Zoo

The morning that the world began
The Lion growled a growl at Man.

And I suspect the Lion might
(If he'd been closer) have tried a bite.

I think that's as it ought to be
And not as it was taught to me.

I think the Lion has a right
To growl a growl and bite a bite.

And if the Lion bothered Adam,
He should have growled right back at 'im.

The way to treat a Lion right
Is growl for growl and bite for bite.

True, the Lion is better fit
For biting than for being bit.

But if you look him in the eye
You'll find the Lion's rather shy.

He really wants someone to pet him.
The trouble is: his teeth won't let him.

He has a heart of gold beneath
But the Lion just can't trust his teeth.

John Ciardi

The Bat

Being a mammal, I have less care than birds,
Being a flight-borne creature, need no home,
So while the beaver builds its, robin its nest,
I hook my hind feet into a wall or ceiling
And hang there looking at the world made silly
By being turned around and upside-down.
Sleep, sleep is my nourishment, I sleep
All day, all winter, and my young's but one.
At first I fly with it at my breast, even hunting,
But if it bores me I hang it on a wall
And go alone, enjoying insects frankly.
Tons, tons, I devour tons of insects, half
Of my weight is insects eaten within one night,
Yet cleverer than the swift or swallow, I deploy
Twist, turn, dodge, catch mosquitoes one by one.
And if the human family finds me odd,
No odder they, locked in their crazy yards.

Ruth Herschberger

The Bat

By day the bat is cousin to the mouse.
He likes the attic of an aging house.

His fingers make a hat about his head.
His pulse beat is so slow we think him dead.

He loops in crazy figures half the night
Among the trees that face the corner light.

But when he brushes up against a screen,
We are afraid of what our eyes have seen:

For something is amiss or out of place
When mice with wings can wear a human face.

Theodore Roethke

Deer Hunt

Because the warden is a cousin, my
mountain friends hunt in summer when the deer
cherish each rattler-ridden spring, and I
have waited hours by a pool in fear
that manhood would require I shoot or that
the steady drip of the hill would dull my ear
to a snake whispering near the log I sat
upon, and listened to the yelping cheer
of dogs and men resounding ridge to ridge.
I flinched at every lonely rifle crack,
my knuckles whitening where I gripped the edge
of age and clung, like retching, sinking back,
then gripping once again the monstrous gun—
since I, to be a man, had taken one.

Judson Jerome

36

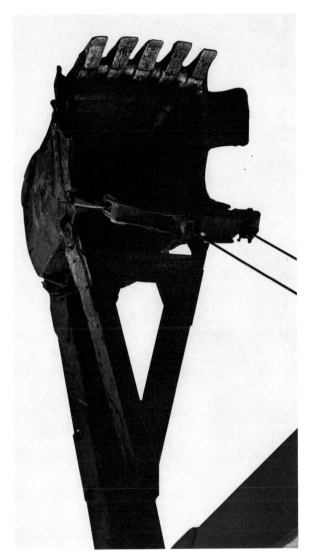

Steam Shovel

The dinosaurs are not all dead.
I saw one raise its iron head
To watch me walking down the road
Beyond our house today.
Its jaws were dripping with a load
Of earth and grass that it had cropped.
It must have heard me where I stopped,
Snorted white steam my way,
And stretched its long neck out to see,
And chewed, and grinned quite amiably.

Charles Malam

The Toaster

A silver-scaled Dragon with jaws flaming red
Sits at my elbow and toasts my bread.
I hand him fat slices, and then, one by one,
He hands them back when he sees they are done.

William Jay Smith

On Watching the Construction
of a Skyscraper

Nothing sings from these orange trees,
Rindless steel as smooth as sapling skin,
Except a crane's brief wheeze
And all the muffled, clanking din
Of rivets nosing in like bees.

Burton Raffel

Apartment House

A filing-cabinet of human lives
Where people swarm like bees in tunneled hives,
Each to his own cell in the towered comb,
Identical and cramped—we call it home.

Gerald Raftery

The Builders   *By Sara Henderson Hay*

I told them a thousand times if I told them once:
Stop fooling around, I said, with straw and sticks;
They won't hold up; you're taking an awful chance.
Brick is the stuff to build with, solid bricks.
You want to be impractical, go ahead.
But just remember, I told them; wait and see.
You're making a big mistake. Awright, I said,
But when the wolf comes, don't come running to me.

The funny thing is, they didn't. There they sat,
One in his crummy yellow shack, and one
Under his roof of twigs, and the wolf ate
Them, hair and hide. Well, what is done is done.
But I'd been willing to help them, all along,
If only they'd once admitted they were wrong.

Transcontinent   *By Donald Hall*

Where the cities end, the
dumps grow the oil-can shacks
from Portland, Maine,

to Seattle. Broken
cars rust in Troy, New York,
and Cleveland Heights.

On the train, the people
eat candy bars, and watch,
or fall asleep.

When they look outside and
see cars and shacks, they know
they're nearly there.

Advice to Travelers

A burro once, sent by express,
His shipping ticket on his bridle,
Ate up his name and his address,
And in some warehouse, standing idle,
He waited till he like to died.
The moral hardly needs the showing:
Don't keep things locked up deep inside—
Say who you are and where you're going.

Walker Gibson

Crossing

By
Philip
Booth

STOP   LOOK   LISTEN
as gate stripes swing down,
count the cars hauling distance
upgrade through town:
warning whistle, bellclang,
engine eating steam,
engineer waving,
a fast-freight dream:
B&M boxcar,
boxcar again,
Frisco gondola,
eight-nine-ten,
Erie and Wabash,
Seaboard, U.P.,
Pennsy tankcar,
twenty-two, three,
Phoebe Snow, B&O,
thirty-four, five,
Santa Fe cattle
shipped alive,
red cars, yellow cars,
orange cars, black,
Youngstown steel
down to Mobile
on Rock Island track,
fifty-nine, sixty,
hoppers of coke,
Anaconda copper,
hotbox smoke,
eighty-eight,
red-ball freight,
Rio Grande,
Nickel Plate,
Hiawatha,
Lackawanna,
rolling fast
and loose,
ninety-seven,
coal car,
boxcar,
CABOOSE!

Crossing Kansas by Train

By Donald Justice

The telephone poles
have been holding their
arms out
a long time now
to birds
that will not
settle there
but pass with
strange cawings
westward to
where dark trees
gather about
a waterhole. This
is Kansas. The
mountains start here
just behind
the closed eyes
of a farmer's
sons asleep
in their workclothes.

African Sunrise

Sky
Over the last star;
The parrot-winds
Sharp-beaked with yellow
Nipping the bunched date palms . . .

Now the camels
Open their beeswax eyes
And raise long necks,
Rutted sound in their throats—
Camels, pock-marking the sand with spread knees,
Lifting the odor of under-body with them.

Sun—
The burn of it
Hot-coined to each eyelid,
And desert-stretched,
      the caravan of hours
         not yet begun.

Gertrude May Lutz

Central
Park
Tourney

By Mildred Weston

Cars
In the Park
With long spear lights
Ride at each other
Like armored knights;
Rush,
Miss the mark,
Pierce the dark,
Dash by!
Another two
Try.

Staged
In the Park
From dusk
To dawn,
The tourney goes on:
Rush,
Miss the mark,
Pierce the dark,
Dash by!
Another two
Try.

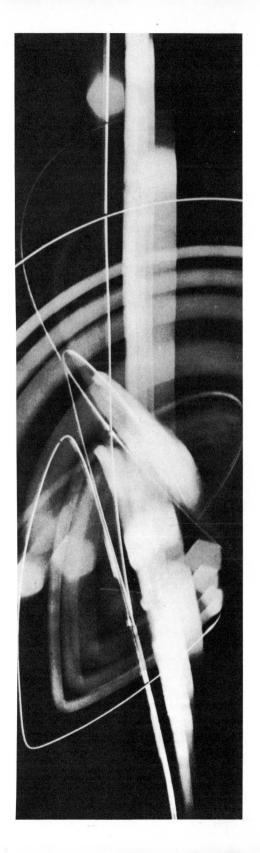

August from My Desk

It is hot today, dry enough for cutting grain,
and I am drifting back to North Dakota
where butterflies are all gone brown with wheat dust.

And where some boy,
red-faced, sweating, chafed,
too young to be dying this way
steers a laborious, self-propelled combine,
and dreams of cities, and blizzards—
and airplanes.

With the white silk scarf of his sleeve
he shines and shines his goggles,
he checks his meters, checks his flaps,
screams contact at his dreamless father,
and, engines roaring,
he pulls back the stick

and hurtles into the sun.

Roland Flint

Kansas Boy

This Kansas boy who never saw the sea
Walks through the young corn rippling at his knee
As sailors walk; and when the grain grows higher
Watches the dark waves leap with greener fire
Than ever oceans hold. He follows ships,
Tasting the bitter spray upon his lips,
For in his blood up-stirs the salty ghost
Of one who sailed a storm-bound English coast.
Across wide fields he hears the sea winds crying,
Shouts at the crows—and dreams of white gulls flying.

Ruth Lechlitner

Wonder Wander

*in the afternoon the children walk like ducks
like geese
like from here to there
eyeing bird-trees puppy dogs candy windows
sun balls ice cream wagons
lady bugs rose bushes fenced yards vacant lots
tall buildings
and other things
big business men take big business walks
wear big business clothes
carry big business briefcases talk about
big business affairs in
big business voices
young girls walk pretty on the streets
stroll the avenues linger by
shop windows wedding rings lady hats
shiny dresses fancy shoes
whisper like turkey hens passing the time
young men stride on parade dream headed
wild eyed eating up the world
with deep glances rubbing empty fingers
in their empty pockets and
planning
me, I wander around soft-shoed easy-legged
watching the scene as it goes
finding things sea-gull feathers pink baby roses
every time I see a letter on the sidewalk
I stop and look it might be
        for me*

Lenore Kandel

Reflections Dental

How pure, how beautiful, how fine
Do teeth on television shine!
No flutist flutes, no dancer twirls,
But comes equipped with matching pearls.
Gleeful announcers all are born
With sets like rows of hybrid corn.
Clowns, critics, clergy, commentators,
Ventriloquists and roller skaters,
M.C.s who beat their palms together,
The girl who diagrams the weather,
The crooner crooning for his supper—
All flash white treasures, lower and upper.
With miles of smiles the airwaves teem,
And each an orthodontist's dream.

'Twould please my eye as gold a miser's—
One charmer with uncapped incisors.

Phyllis McGinley

The Microscope

Anton Leeuwenhoek was Dutch.
He sold pincushions, cloth, and such.
The waiting townsfolk fumed and fussed
As Anton's dry goods gathered dust.

He worked, instead of tending store,
At grinding special lenses for
A microscope. Some of the things
He looked at were:
                              mosquitoes' wings,
the hairs of sheep, the legs of lice,
the skin of people, dogs, and mice;
ox eyes, spiders' spinning gear,
fishes' scales, a little smear
of his own blood,
                              and best of all,
the unknown, busy, very small
bugs that swim and bump and hop
inside a simple water drop.

Impossible! Most Dutchmen said.
This Anton's crazy in the head.
We ought to ship him off to Spain.
He says he's seen a housefly's brain.
He says the water that we drink
Is full of bugs. He's mad, we think!

They called him dumkopf, which means dope.
That's how we got the microscope.

                              Maxine Kumin

53

Child

on Top

of a

Greenhouse

The wind billowing out the seat of my britches,
My feet crackling splinters of glass and dried putty,
The half-grown chrysanthemums staring up like accusers,
Up through the streaked glass, flashing with sunlight,
A few white clouds all rushing eastward,
A line of elms plunging and tossing like horses,
And everyone, everyone pointing up and shouting!

Theodore Roethke

Loneliness

I was about to go, and said so;
And I had almost started for the door.
But he was all alone in the sugar-house,
And more lonely than he'd ever been before.
We'd talked for half an hour, almost,
About the price of sugar, and how I like my school,
And he had made me drink some syrup hot,
Telling me it was better that way than when cool.

And I agreed, and thanked him for it,
And said good-bye, and was about to go.
Want to see where I was born?
He asked me quickly. How to say no?

The sugar-house looked over miles of valley.
He pointed with a sticky finger to a patch of snow
Where he was born. The house, he said, was gone.
I can understand these people better, now I know.

Brooks Jenkins

Indians

*By
John
Fandel*

Margaret mentioned Indians,
And I began to think about Indians—

Indians once living
Where now we are living—

And I thought how little I know
About Indians. Oh, I know

What I have heard. Not much,
When I think how much

I wonder about them,
When a mere mention of them,

Indians, starts me. I
Think of their wigwams. I

Think of canoes. I think
Of quick arrows. I think

Of things Indian. And still
I think of their bright, still

Summers, when these hills
And meadows on these hills

Shone in the morning
Suns before this morning.

Arithmetic   *By Carl Sandburg*

*Arithmetic is where numbers fly like pigeons in and out of your
head.*
*Arithmetic tells you how many you lose or win if you know how
many you had before you lost or won.*
*Arithmetic is seven eleven all good children go to heaven—or five
six bundle of sticks.*
*Arithmetic is numbers you squeeze from your head to your hand
to your pencil to your paper till you get the answer.*
*Arithmetic is where the answer is right and everything is nice and
you can look out of the window and see the blue sky—or the
answer is wrong and you have to start all over and try again
and see how it comes out this time.*
*If you take a number and double it and double it again and then
double it a few more times, the number gets bigger and bigger
and goes higher and higher and only arithmetic can tell you
what the number is when you decide to quit doubling.*
*Arithmetic is where you have to multiply—and you carry the
multiplication table in your head and hope you won't lose it.*
*If you have two animal crackers, one good and one bad, and you
eat one and a striped zebra with streaks all over him eats the
other, how many animal crackers will you have if somebody
offers you five six seven and you say No no no and you say
Nay nay nay and you say Nix nix nix?*
*If you ask your mother for one fried egg for breakfast and she
gives you two fried eggs and you eat both of them, who is
better in arithmetic, you or your mother?*

Husbands

and

Wives

Husbands and wives
  With children between them
Sit in the subway;
  So I have seen them.

One word only
  From station to station;
So much talk for
  So close a relation.

Miriam Hershenson

This Is Just to Say

I have eaten
the plums
that were in
the icebox

and which
you were probably
saving
for breakfast

Forgive me
they were delicious
so sweet
and so cold.

William Carlos Williams

The Ne'er-Do-Well When Enoch should have been at work,
He might be fishing in the creek,
Or when the dewberries were ripe,
He'd leave his plowing for a week.
He'd take an hour to smoke a pipe,
Sitting with legs crossed like a Turk.

And yet the banker, looking grim
When Enoch with a note past due
Had left his corn patch to the cows,
Sought a persimmon grove he knew
And, finding Enoch in the boughs,
Stared long and wistfully at him.

Arthur M. Sampley

Meditatio When I carefully consider the curious habits of dogs
I am compelled to conclude
That man is the superior animal.

When I consider the curious habits of man
I confess, my friend, I am puzzled.

Ezra Pound

Summons

Keep me from going to sleep too soon
Or if I go to sleep too soon
Come wake me up. Come any hour
Of night. Come whistling up the road.
Stomp on the porch. Bang on the door.
Make me get out of bed and come
And let you in and light a light.
Tell me the northern lights are on
And make me look. Or tell me clouds
Are doing something to the moon
They never did before, and show me.
See that I see. Talk to me till
I'm half as wide awake as you
And start to dress wondering why
I ever went to bed at all.
Tell me the walking is superb.
Not only tell me but persuade me.
You know I'm not too hard persuaded.

Robert Francis

Ancient History

By Arthur Guiterman

I hope the old Romans
Had painful abdomens.

I hope that the Greeks
Had toothache for weeks.

I hope the Egyptians
Had chronic conniptions.

I hope that the Arabs
Were bitten by scarabs.

I hope that the Vandals
Had thorns in their sandals.

I hope that the Persians
Had gout in all versions.

I hope that the Medes
Were kicked by their steeds.

They started the fuss
And left it to us!

On the Vanity of Earthly Greatness

By Arthur Guiterman

The tusks that clashed in mighty brawls
Of mastodons, are billiard balls.

The sword of Charlemagne the Just
Is ferric oxide, known as rust.

The grizzly bear whose potent hug
Was feared by all, is now a rug.

Great Caesar's dead and on the shelf,
And I don't feel so well myself!

Dust

Agatha Morley
All her life
Grumbled at dust
Like a good wife.

Dust on a table,
Dust on a chair,
Dust on a mantel
She couldn't bear.

She forgave faults
In man and child
But a dusty shelf
Would set her wild.

She bore with sin
Without protest,
But dust thoughts preyed
Upon her rest.

Agatha Morley
Is sleeping sound
Six feet under
The mouldy ground.

Six feet under
The earth she lies
With dust at her feet
And dust in her eyes.

Sydney King Russell

Rebecca

Who slammed Doors for Fun and Perished Miserably

A Trick that everyone abhors
In Little Girls is slamming Doors.
A Wealthy Banker's little Daughter
Who lived in Palace Green, Bayswater
(By name Rebecca Offendort),
Was given to this Furious Sport.
She would deliberately go
And Slam the door like Billy-Ho!
To make her Uncle Jacob start.
She was not really bad at heart,
But only rather rude and wild:
She was an aggravating child.

It happened that a Marble Bust
Of Abraham was standing just
Above the Door this little Lamb
Had carefully prepared to Slam,
And down it came! It knocked her flat!
It laid her out! She looked like that!

. . . .

Her funeral Sermon (which was long
And followed by a Sacred Song)
Mentioned her Virtues, it is true,
But dwelt upon her Vices too,
And showed the Dreadful End of One
Who goes and slams the door for Fun.

Hilaire Belloc

Bones

Said Mr. Smith, "I really cannot
   Tell you, Dr. Jones—
The most peculiar pain I'm in—
   I think it's in my bones."

Said Dr. Jones, "Oh, Mr. Smith,
   That's nothing. Without doubt
We have a simple cure for that;
   It is to take them out."

He laid forthwith poor Mr. Smith
   Close-clamped upon the table,
And, cold as stone, took out his bone
   As fast as he was able.

And Smith said, "Thank you, thank you, thank you,"
   And wished him a good-day;
And with his parcel 'neath his arm
   He slowly moved away.

Walter de la Mare

Overheard on a Saltmarsh

Nymph, nymph, what are your beads?

Green glass, goblin. Why do you stare at them?

Give them me.

> *No.*

Give them me. Give them me.

> *No.*

Then I will howl all night in the reeds,
Lie in the mud and howl for them.

Goblin, why do you love them so?

They are better than stars or water,
Better than voices of winds that sing,
Better than any man's fair daughter,
Your green glass beads on a silver ring.

Hush, I stole them out of the moon.

Give me your beads, I want them.

> *No.*

I will howl in a deep lagoon
For your green glass beads, I love them so.
Give them me. Give them.

> *No.*

Harold Monro

Résumé

Razors pain you;
Rivers are damp;
Acids stain you;
And drugs cause cramp.
Guns aren't lawful;
Nooses give;
Gas smells awful;
You might as well live.

Dorothy Parker

Lost   *By Carl Sandburg*

Desolate and lone
All night long on the lake
Where fog trails and mist creeps,
The whistle of a boat
Calls and cries unendingly,
Like some lost child
In tears and trouble
Hunting the harbor's breast
And the harbor's eyes.

Fifteen
South of the Bridge on Seventeenth
I found back of the willows one summer
day a motorcycle with engine running
as it lay on its side, ticking over
slowly in the high grass. I was fifteen.

I admired all that pulsing gleam, the
shiny flanks, the demure headlights
fringed where it lay; I led it gently
to the road and stood with that
companion, ready and friendly. I was fifteen.

We could find the end of a road, meet
the sky on out Seventeenth. I thought about
hills, and patting the handle got back a
confident opinion. On the bridge we indulged
a forward feeling, a tremble. I was fifteen.

Thinking, back farther in the grass I found
the owner, just coming to, where he had flipped
over the rail. He had blood on his hand, was pale—
I helped him walk to his machine. He ran his hand
over it, called me good man, roared away.

I stood there, fifteen.

William Stafford

Interlude III   *Writing, I crushed an insect with my nail*
And thought nothing at all. A bit of wing
Caught my eye then, a gossamer so frail

And exquisite, I saw in it a thing
That scorned the grossness of the thing I wrote.
It hung upon my finger like a sting.

A leg I noticed next, fine as a mote,
"And on this frail eyelash he walked," I said,
"And climbed and walked like any mountain-goat."

And in this mood I sought the little head,
But it was lost; then in my heart a fear
Cried out, "A life—why beautiful, why dead!"

It was a mite that held itself most dear,
So small I could have drowned it with a tear.

Karl Shapiro

War   *Dawn came slowly,*
almost not at all.
The sun crept over the hill
cautiously
fearful of being hit
by mortar fire.

Dan Roth

71

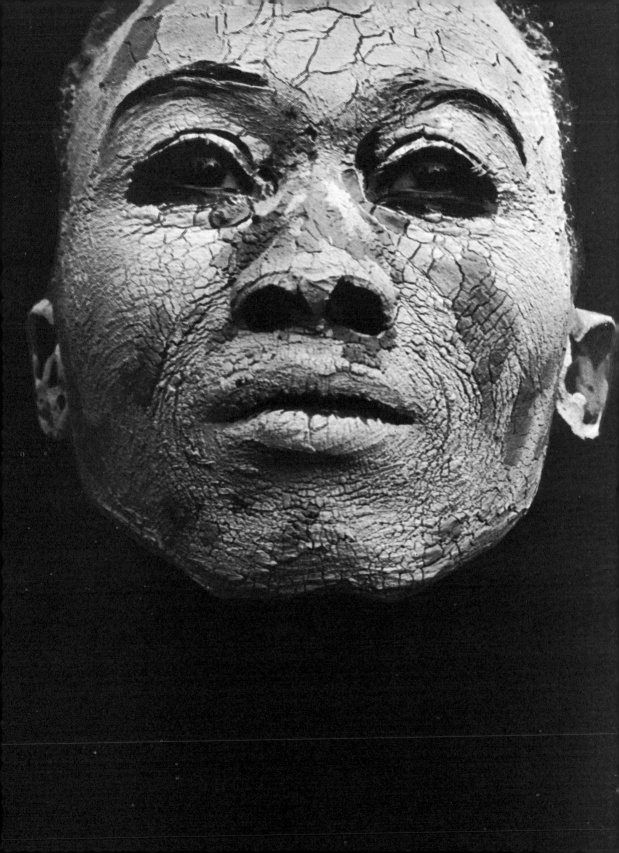

Too Blue

I got those sad old weary blues.
I don't know where to turn.
I don't know where to go.
Nobody cares about you
When you sink so low.

What shall I do?
What shall I say?
Shall I take a gun and
Put myself away?

I wonder if
One bullet would do?
Hard as my head is,
It would probably take two.

But I ain't got
Neither bullet nor gun—
And I'm too blue
To look for one.

Langston Hughes

from **Two Jazz Poems**

yeah here am i
am standing
at the crest of a tallest
hill with a trumpet
in my hand & dark
glasses
on.

    bearded & bereted i proudly stand!
       but there are no eyes to see me.
  i send down cool sounds!
       but there are no ears to hear me.

              Carl Wendell Hines, Jr.

A Coney Island Life

Having lived a Coney Island life
on rollercoaster ups and downs
and seen my helium hopes
break skyward without me,
now arms filled with dolls
I threw so much for
I take perhaps my last ride
on this planet-carousel
and ask
how many more times round
I have
to catch that brass-ring-sun
before the game is up.

        James L. Weil

Carmel Point

I watched a sea anemone
The color of green jade
Shadowed under water.

I saw a daring crab,
Unafraid and young
Touch the velvet petals
Of that princess under water.
Softly she took him in,
Softly she sighed and closed.
The little crab was hushed and still—
Never would he swim again
Under crevice, under weed,
Under green and colored water.

Softly she opened—
That princess of rare jade.
Softly she gave him back
Sucked of all his pearly flesh
Sucked of all his salty blood.

I ran away to tell my dad,
"Let's go home," I said,
"I am sorry to be born,
I am afraid of many things."

Margaret Phyllis MacSweeney

Forgive My Guilt

Not always sure what things called sins may be,
I am sure of one sin I have done.
It was years ago, and I was a boy,
I lay in the frostflowers with a gun,
The air ran blue as the flowers, I held my breath,
Two birds on golden legs slim as dream things
Ran like quicksilver on the golden sand,
My gun went off, they ran with broken wings
Into the sea, I ran to fetch them in,
But they swam with their heads high out to sea,
They cried like two sorrowful high flutes,
With jagged ivory bones where wings should be.

For days I heard them when I walked that headland
Crying out to their kind in the blue,
The other plovers were going over south
On silver wings leaving these broken two.
The cries went out one day; but I still hear them
Over all the sounds of sorrow in war or peace
I ever have heard, time cannot drown them,
Those slender flutes of sorrow never cease.
Two airy things forever denied the air!
I never knew how their lives at last were spilt,
But I have hoped for years all that is wild,
Airy, and beautiful will forgive my guilt.

Robert P. Tristram Coffin

The Term   *By William Carlos Williams*

*A rumpled sheet
of brown paper
about the length*

*and apparent bulk
of a man was
rolling with the*

*wind slowly over
and over in
the street as*

*a car drove down
upon it and
crushed it to*

*the ground. Unlike
a man it rose
again rolling*

*with the wind over
and over to be as
it was before.*

Sonic Boom

By John Updike

I'm sitting in the living room,
When, up above, the Thump of Doom
Resounds. Relax. It's sonic boom.

The ceiling shudders at the clap,
The mirrors tilt, the rafters snap,
And Baby wakens from his nap.

"Hush, babe. Some pilot we equip,
Giving the speed of sound the slip,
Has cracked the air like a penny whip."

Our world is far from frightening; I
No longer strain to read the sky
Where moving fingers (jet planes) fly.
Our world seems much too tame to die.

And if it does, with one more pop,
I shan't look up to see it drop.

Hey Diddle Diddle

Hey diddle diddle,
The physicists fiddle,
The Bleep jumped over the moon.
The little dog laughed to see such fun
And died the following June.

Paul Dehn

Little Miss Muffet

Little Miss Muffet
Crouched on a tuffet,
Collecting her shell-shocked wits.
There dropped (from a glider)
An H-bomb beside her—
Which frightened Miss Muffet to bits.

Paul Dehn

Earth   *By Oliver Herford*

If this little world tonight
    Suddenly should fall through space
In a hissing, headlong flight,
    Shrivelling from off its face,
As it falls into the sun,
    In an instant every trace
Of the little crawling things—
    Ants, philosophers, and lice,
Cattle, cockroaches, and kings,
    Beggars, millionaires, and mice,
Men and maggots all as one
As it falls into the sun. . . .
Who can say but at the same
    Instant from some planet far
A child may watch us and exclaim:
    "See the pretty shooting star!"

Earth   *By John Hall Wheelock*

"A planet doesn't explode of itself," said drily
The Martian astronomer, gazing off into the air—
"That they were able to do it is proof that highly
Intelligent beings must have been living there."

Southbound on the Freeway

A tourist came in from Orbitville,
parked in the air, and said:

The creatures of this star
are made of metal and glass.

Through the transparent parts
you can see their guts.

Their feet are round and roll
on diagrams or long

measuring tapes, dark
with white lines.

They have four eyes.
The two in back are red.

Sometimes you can see a five-eyed
one, with a red eye turning

on the top of his head.
He must be special—

the others respect him
and go slow

when he passes, winding
among them from behind.

They all hiss as they glide,
like inches, down the marked

tapes. Those soft shapes,
shadowy inside

the hard bodies—are they
their guts or their brains?

May Swenson

Fueled

Fueled
by a million
man-made
wings of fire—
the rocket tore a tunnel
through the sky—
and everybody cheered.
Fueled
only by a thought from God—
the seedling
urged its way
through the thicknesses of black—
and as it pierced
the heavy ceiling of the soil—
and launched itself
up into outer space—
no
one
even
clapped.

Marcie Hans

Unsatisfied Yearning

Down in the silent hallway
Scampers the dog about,
And whines, and barks, and scratches,
In order to get out.

Once in the glittering starlight,
He straightway doth begin
To set up a doleful howling
In order to get in!

Richard Kendall Munkittrick

Puppy   Catch and shake the cobra garden hose.
Scramble on panicky paws and flee
The hiss of tensing nozzle nose,
Or stalk that snobbish bee.

The back yard world is vast as park
With belly-tickle grass and stun
Of sudden sprinkler squalls that are
Rainbows to the yap yap sun.

Robert L. Tyler

Sunning   Old Dog lay in the summer sun
Much too lazy to rise and run.
He flapped an ear
At a buzzing fly.
He winked a half opened
Sleepy eye.
He scratched himself
On an itching spot,
As he dozed on the porch
Where the sun was hot.
He whimpered a bit
From force of habit
While he lazily dreamed
Of chasing a rabbit.
But Old Dog happily lay in the sun
Much too lazy to rise and run.

James S. Tippett

Elegy for Jog *Stiff-dog death, all froth on a bloody chin,*
sniffs at the curb. Skinny-man death, his master,
opens the traffic's hedge to let him in.
Jog was his name, silliness his disaster.
He wasn't satisfied to scare the truck:
he had to bite the tire. Fools have no luck.

John Ciardi

Catalogue

By
Rosalie Moore

Cats sleep fat and walk thin.
Cats, when they sleep, slump;
When they wake, stretch and begin
Over, pulling their ribs in.
Cats walk thin.

Cats wait in a lump,
Jump in a streak.
Cats, when they jump, are sleek
As a grape slipping its skin—
They have technique.
Oh, cats don't creak.
They sneak.

Cats sleep fat.
They spread out comfort underneath them
Like a good mat,
As if they picked the place
And then sat;
You walk around one
As if he were the City Hall
After that.

If male,
A cat is apt to sing on a major scale;
This concert is for everybody, this
Is wholesale.
For a baton, he wields a tail.

(He is also found,
When happy, to resound
With an enclosed and private sound.)

A cat condenses.
He pulls in his tail to go under bridges,
And himself to go under fences.
Cats fit
In any size box or kit,
And if a large pumpkin grew under one,
He could arch over it.

When everyone else is just ready to go out,
The cat is just ready to come in.
He's not where he's been.
Cats sleep fat and walk thin.

Poem

*As the cat
climbed over
the top of*

*the jamcloset
first the right
forefoot*

*carefully
then the hind
stepped down*

*into the pit of
the empty
flowerpot.*

  William Carlos Williams

On a Night of Snow

Cat, if you go outdoors you must walk in the snow.
You will come back with little white shoes on your feet,
Little white slippers of snow that have heels of sleet.
Stay by the fire, my Cat. Lie still, do not go.
See how the flames are leaping and hissing low.
I will bring you a saucer of milk like a marguerite,
So white and so smooth, so spherical and so sweet.
Stay with me, Cat. Outdoors the wild winds blow.

Outdoors the wild winds blow, Mistress, and dark is the night.
Strange voices cry in the trees, intoning strange lore,
And more than cats move, lit by our eyes' green light,
On silent feet where the meadow grasses hang hoar—
Mistress, there are portents abroad of magic and might,
And things that are yet to be done. Open the door!

Elizabeth Coatsworth

For a Dead Kitten

Put the rubber mouse away,
Pick the spools up from the floor,
What was velvet-shod, and gay,
Will not want them any more.

What was warm, is strangely cold.
Whence dissolved the little breath?
How could this small body hold
So immense a thing as Death?

Sara Henderson Hay

Oz.

Whoever discounts
the ounce
as one of the smallest amounts
has never met up with the ounce
that belongs to the cat family.

This jungle ounce
will jounce
you out of complacency.
If you try to trounce
this ounce,
you will be chastened hastily;
for this ounce
does more than flounce;
this ounce can bounce,
this ounce can pounce.

So if you meet up with an ounce,
announce yourself as a friend,
or it might be The End.

P.S. Better not take a chounce.

Eve Merriam

April   *By Marcia Masters*

It's lemonade, it's lemonade, it's daisy.
It's a roller-skating, scissor-grinding day;
It's gingham-waisted, chocolate flavored, lazy,
With the children flower-scattered at their play.

It's the sun like watermelon,
And the sidewalks overlaid
With a glaze of yellow yellow
Like a jar of marmalade.

It's the mower gently mowing,
And the stars like startled glass,
While the mower keeps on going
Through a waterfall of grass.

Then the rich magenta evening
Like a sauce upon the walk,
And the porches softly swinging
With a hammockful of talk.

It's the hobo at the corner
With his lilac-sniffing gait,
And the shy departing thunder
Of the fast departing skate.

It's lemonade, it's lemonade, it's April!
A water sprinkler, puddle winking time,
When a boy who peddles slowly, with a smile remote and holy,
Sells you April chocolate flavored for a dime.

in Just-

in Just-
spring   when the world is mud-
luscious the little
lame balloonman

whistles   far   and wee

and eddieandbill come
running from marbles and
piracies and it's
spring

when the world is puddle-wonderful

the queer
old balloonman whistles
far   and   wee
and bettyandisbel come dancing

from hop-scotch and jump-rope and

it's
spring
and
   the

     goat-footed

balloonMan   whistles
far
and
wee

              E. E. Cummings

The Child's Morning

Gangway for violets,
Old snow in the corner.
Sun after a rise of rain
Over cuttlebone cloud.
Sun in the brook running
Green with watercress
Sun on the spade—
We shovel out crocuses.
Up the concrete walk
Under surf of rollerskates
The hail of jacks,
Kiss-click of aggies.
We summon with jumpropes
Sap in the trees,
With ·bat-knock of ball
And the thudding glove.
That clang of schoolbells
We answer with answers:
Tall immaculate silence
Of colored kites.

Winfield Townley Scott

Four Little Foxes

Speak gently, Spring, and make no sudden sound;
For in my windy valley, yesterday I found
New-born foxes squirming on the ground—
    Speak gently.

Walk softly, March, forbear the bitter blow;
Her feet within a trap, her blood upon the snow,
The four little foxes saw their mother go—
    Walk softly.

Go lightly, Spring, oh, give them no alarm;
When I covered them with boughs to shelter them from harm,
The thin blue foxes suckled at my arm—
    Go lightly.

Step softly, March, with your rampant hurricane;
Nuzzling one another, and whimpering with pain,
The new little foxes are shivering in the rain—
    Step softly.

Lew Sarett

Four Ducks on a Pond

By

William Allingham.

Four ducks on a pond,
A grass-bank beyond,
A blue sky of spring,
White clouds on the wing;
What a little thing
To remember for years—
To remember with tears!

Counting-Out Rhyme

By

Edna St. Vincent Millay

Silver bark of beech, and sallow
Bark of yellow birch and yellow
Twig of willow.

Stripe of green in moosewood maple,
Colour seen in leaf of apple,
Bark of popple.

Wood of popple pale as moonbeam,
Wood of oak for yoke and barn-beam,
Wood of hornbeam.

Silver bark of beech, and hollow
Stem of elder, tall and yellow
Twig of willow.

April

By

Yvor Winters

The little goat
crops
new grass lying down
leaps up eight inches
into air and
lands on four feet.
Not a tremor—
solid in the
spring and serious
he walks away.

Swift things are beautiful:
Swallows and deer,
And lightning that falls
Bright-veined and clear,
Rivers and meteors,
Wind in the wheat,
The strong-withered horse,
The runner's sure feet.

Swift Things Are Beautiful   *By Elizabeth Coatsworth*

And slow things are beautiful:
The closing of day,
The pause of the wave
That curves downward to spray,
The ember that crumbles,
The opening flower,
And the ox that moves on
In the quiet of power.

Fortune
                              Fortune

                                    has its cookies to give out

            which is a good thing

                              since it's been a long time since

                  that summer in Brooklyn
            when they closed off the street
                  one hot day
                  and the

                                          FIREMEN

                                          turned on their hoses

            and all the kids ran out in it

                        in the middle of the street

            and there were

                              maybe a couple dozen of us

                                          out there

with the water squirting up
                    to the

                    sky

                    and all over
                              us
    there was maybe only six of us
                          kids altogether
        running around in our
                    barefeet and birthday
        suits
            and I remember Molly but then

    the firemen stopped squirting their hoses
        all of a sudden and went
            back in
            their firehouse
            and
        started playing pinochle again
            just as if nothing
            had ever
                    happened
while I remember Molly
            looked at me and

    ran in

because I guess really we were the only ones there

                    Lawrence Ferlinghetti

Fish

Story

Count this among my heartfelt wishes:
To hear a fish tale told by fishes
And stand among the fish who doubt
The honor of a fellow trout,
And watch the bulging of their eyes
To hear of imitation flies
And worms with rather droopy looks
Stuck through with hateful, horrid hooks,
And fishermen they fled all day from
(As big as this) and got away from.

Richard Armour

Angler's Choice

By H. J. Gottlieb

These he cast
Where the pool lay still
Under a lichened ledge:
Silver Doctor, Olive Quill,
Ibis, Lady Beaverkill,
        And a Dark Blue Sedge.

These he chose
For the stony flat
Spanned by the covered bridge:
Royal Coachman, Cahill, Gnat,
March Brown, Little Marryat,
        And a Berry Midge.

These he tried
In the fading light
Down by the alder thicket:
Yellow Sally, Sandy Mite,
Wickham's Fancy; Cocky Knight,
        And a real, live cricket.

The Fisher

By Lyle Glazier

At half past four, mornings in June,
He met the sliding, whispery sound
Of Four Mile Brook, and liked the tune,
And liked the log road, morning-hushed;
His bare feet liked the dew-soaked ground.

At half past ten, he was headed for home,
Having tried his last last-hole for luck;
The heat and noise of the day had come,
But his bones were cool with the brookside shade,
And his ears kept the whirlpool's silvery suck.

Hunting

Song

By Donald

Finkel

The fox came lolloping, lolloping,
Lolloping. His tongue hung out
And his ears were high.
He was like death at the end of a string
When he came to the hollow
Log. Ran in one side
And out of the other. O
He was sly.

The hounds came tumbling, tumbling,
Tumbling. Their heads were low
And their eyes were red.
The sound of their breath was louder than death
When they came to the hollow
Log. They held at one end
But a bitch found the scent. O
They were mad.

The hunter came galloping, galloping,
Galloping. All damp was his mare
From her hooves to her mane.
His coat and his mouth were redder than death
When he came to the hollow
Log. He took in the rein
And over he went. O
He was fine.

The log, he just lay there, alone in
The clearing. No fox nor hound
Nor mounted man
Saw his black round eyes in their perfect disguise
(As the ends of a hollow
Log). He watched death go through him,
Around him, and over him. O
He was wise.

The Trap

By William Beyer

"That red fox,
Back in the furthest field,
Caught in my hidden trap,
Was half mad with fear.
During the night
He must have ripped his foot
From the cold steel.
I saw him early this morning,
Dragging his hurt leg,
Bleeding a path across the gold wheat,
Whining with the pain;
His eyes like cracked marbles.
I followed as he moved,
His thin body pulled to one side
In a weird helplessness.
He hit the wire fence,
Pushing through it
Into the deep, morning corn,
And was gone."
The old man looked around the kitchen
To see if anyone was listening.
"Crazy red fox,
Will kill my chickens no longer.
Will die somewhere in hiding."
He lit the brown tobacco carefully,
Watching the blue smoke rise and disappear
In the movement of the air.
Scratching his red nose slowly,
Thinking something grave for a long moment,
He stared out of the bright window.
"He won't last long with that leg," he said.
The old man turned his head
To see if his wife was listening.
But she was deep in thought,
Her stained fingers
Pressing red berries in a pie.
He turned his white head
Toward the open window again.
"Guess I'll ride into the back field, first thing.
Some mighty big corn back there this year.
Mighty big corn."
His wife looked up from her work,
Smiled almost secretly to herself,
And finished packing the ripe berries
Into the pale crust.

Fireworks
By Babette Deutsch

Not guns, not thunder, but a flutter of clouded drums
That announce a fiesta: abruptly, fiery needles
Circumscribe on the night boundless chrysanthemums.
Softly, they break apart, they flake away, where
Darkness, on a svelte hiss, swallows them.
Delicate brilliance: a bellflower opens, fades,
In a sprinkle of falling stars.
Night absorbs them
With the sponge of her silence.

The Garden Hose

In the gray evening
I see a long green serpent
With its tail in the dahlias.

It lies in loops across the grass
And drinks softly at the faucet.

I can hear it swallow.

Beatrice Janosco

Lullaby

The long canoe
Toward the shadowy shore,
One . . . two . . .
Three . . . four . . .
The paddle dips,
Turns in the wake,
Pauses, then
Forward again.
Water drips
From the blade to the lake.
Nothing but that,
No sound of wings;
The owl and bat
Are velvet things.
No wind awakes,
No fishes leap;
No rabbits creep
Among the brakes.
The long canoe
At the shadowy shore,
One . . . two . . .
Three . . . four . . .
A murmur now
Under the prow
Where rushes bow
To let us through.
One . . . two . . .
Upon the shore,
Three . . . four . . .
Upon the lake,
No one's awake,
No one's awake,
One . . . two . . .
No one, not even you.

Robert Hillyer

The Base Stealer

By Robert Francis

Poised between going on and back, pulled
Both ways taut like a tightrope-walker,
Fingertips pointing the opposites,
Now bouncing tiptoe like a dropped ball
Or a kid skipping rope, come on, come on,
Running a scattering of steps sidewise,
How he teeters, skitters, tingles, teases,
Taunts them, hovers like an ecstatic bird,
He's only flirting, crowd him, crowd him,
Delicate, delicate, delicate, delicate—now!

Foul Shot

By Edwin A. Hoey

With two 60's stuck on the scoreboard
And two seconds hanging on the clock,
The solemn boy in the center of eyes,
Squeezed by silence,
Seeks out the line with his feet,
Soothes his hands along his uniform,
Gently drums the ball against the floor,
Then measures the waiting net,
Raises the ball on his right hand,
Balances it with his left,
Calms it with fingertips,
Breathes,
Crouches,
Waits,
And then through a stretching of stillness,
Nudges it upward.

The ball
Slides up and out,
Lands,
Leans,
Wobbles,
Wavers,
Hesitates,
Exasperates,
Plays it coy
Until every face begs with unsounding screams—

And then

      And then

            And then,

Right before ROAR-UP,
Dives down and through.

Millions of Strawberries

By Genevieve Taggard

Marcia and I went over the curve,
Eating our way down
Jewels of strawberries we didn't deserve,
Eating our way down.
Till our hands were sticky, and our lips painted,
And over us the hot day fainted,
And we saw snakes,
And got scratched,
And a lust overcame us for the red unmatched
Small buds of berries,
Till we lay down—
Eating our way down—
And rolled in the berries like two little dogs,
Rolled
In the late gold.
And gnats hummed,
And it was cold,
And home we went, home without a berry,
Painted red and brown,
Eating our way down.

Cheers

By Eve Merriam

The frogs and the serpents each had a football team,
and I heard their cheer leaders in my dream:

"Bilgewater, bilgewater," called the frog,
"Bilgewater, bilgewater,
Sis, boom, bog!
Roll 'em off the log,
Slog 'em in the sog,
Swamp'em, swamp'em,
Muck mire quash!"

"Sisyphus, Sisyphus," hissed the snake,
"Sibilant, syllabub,
Syllable-loo-ba-lay.
Scylla and Charybdis,
Sumac, asphodel,
How do you spell Success?
With an S-S-S!"

The Forecast

Perhaps our age has driven us indoors.
We sprawl in the semi-darkness, dreaming sometimes
Of a vague world spinning in the wind.
But we have snapped our locks, pulled down our shades,
Taken all precautions. We shall not be disturbed.
If the earth shakes, it will be on a screen;
And if the prairie wind spills down our streets
And covers us with leaves, the weatherman will tell us.

Dan Jaffe

Mother's Biscuits

In a big bowl she'd fluff in flour,
Make a fist-dent
For buttermilk and lard which she squeezed
Between her fingers
The way a child goes at a mud puddle,
Raking dry flour
From the sides until it mixed right.

She'd give the dough a pat for luck,
Nip a springy bud,
Roll it round and flat-it-down
With a motion
Continued to a grease-shined pan.
Mother's biscuits
Cooked high, crusty, with succulent middles
That took attention
At company dinners; but on kitchen-nights
They were finest
Soaked with pot liquor or gravy.

And those rich biscuits could put a shine
On Sunday patent
That let the Lord know who was there.
A panful stood
Ready as magic at dawn's light:
I'd take some
When leaving late to the schoolbus
And up the road
I'd run, puffing through biscuit crumbs
My haloed breath
Into the skin-sharp morning air.

Freda Quenneville

Two Lives and Others

Beyond the field where crows cawed at a hawk
The road bent down between oaks, pines, and maples:
Maples skimming the air with terra cotta.
The oaks spat acorns over scurries of squirrels.
Moss crunched stiff underfoot, and overhead
The sky was gradually freezing, white across blue.
We hurried our walk through shadows, yet it was
A noticeable sort of afternoon:
We honored a faded robin and considered
The importance of the color gray on bluejays.
A woodchuck, all an urgent clumsiness,
Made his tumbling run, then he saw us,
Plunged, hid, and screamed his whistle of fear.
Round the next bend to twilight we went past
A solitary house, one room lamplighted,
An old man at supper alone facing the wall.
If he was aware of us he gave no sign.
We circled home, that last day before snow.

Winfield Townley Scott

A pheasant cock sprang into view,
A living jewel, up he flew.

His wings laid hold on empty space,
Scorn bulged his eyeballs out with grace.

He was a hymn from tail to beak
With not a tender note or meek.

The Pheasant   *By Robert P. Tristram Coffin*   *Then the gun let out its thunder,*
The bird descended struck with wonder.

He ran a little, then, amazed,
Settled with his head upraised.

The fierceness flowed out of his eyes
And left them meek and large and wise.

Gentleness relaxed his head,
He lay in jewelled feathers, dead.

November Day *By Eleanor Averitt*

*Old haggard wind has
    plucked the trees
Like pheasants, held
    between her knees.
In rows she hangs them,
    bare and neat,
Their brilliant plumage at
    her feet.*

Grey Goose

It was one Sunday mornin'
  Lawd, lawd, lawd![1]
The preacher went a-huntin'!
He carried 'long his shotgun.
Well, 'long come a grey goose.
The gun went off boo-loo
And down come a grey goose.
He was six weeks a-fallin'!
And my wife and yo' wife,
They give him feather-pickin'.
They was six weeks a-pickin',
And they put him on to parboil.
He was six weeks a boilin',
And they put him on the table,
And the knife wouldn't cut him,
Aw, the fork wouldn't stick him.
And they throwed him in the hog-pen,
And the hog couldn't eat him,
Aw, he broke the hog's teeth out.
They tak'n him to the saw mill,
And the saw wouldn't cut him.
Aw, he broke the saw's teeth out.
An' the last time I seed him,
He was flyin' cross de ocean
With a long string o' goslin's.
An' they all goin', "Quack, quack."

[1]This response follows each line.

Wild Goose

He climbs the wind above
*   green clouds of pine,*
Honking to hail the
*   gathering migration,*
And, arching toward the
*   south, pulls to align*
His flight into the great
*   spearhead formation.*

He'll find a bayou land of
*   hidden pools,*
And bask amid lush fern
*   and water lily*
Far from the frozen world
*   of earth-bound fools*
Who, shivering, maintain
*   that geese are silly.*

Curtis Heath

Fall

The geese flying south
In a row long and V-shaped
Pulling in winter.

Sally Andresen

Valentine

By Donald Hall

*Chipmunks jump, and
Greensnakes slither.
Rather burst than
Not be with her.*

*Bluebirds fight, but
Bears are stronger.
We've got fifty
Years or longer.*

*Hoptoads hop, but
Hogs are fatter.
Nothing else but
Us can matter.*

Oregon Winter

The rain begins. This is no summer rain,
Dropping the blotches of wet on the dusty road:
This rain is slow, without thunder or hurry:
There is plenty of time—there will be months of rain.
Lost in the hills, the old gray farmhouses
Hump their backs against it, and smoke from their chimneys
Struggles through weighted air. The sky is sodden with water,
It sags against the hills, and the wild geese,
Wedge-flying, brush the heaviest cloud with their wings.
The farmers move unhurried. The wood is in,
The hay has long been in, the barn lofts piled
Up to the high windows, dripping yellow straws.
There will be plenty of time now, time that will smell of fires,
And drying leather, and catalogues, and apple cores.
The farmers clean their boots, and whittle, and drowse.

Jeanne McGahey

The Stump   *Today they cut down the oak.*
Strong men climbed with ropes
in the brittle tree.
The exhaust of a gasoline saw
was blue in the branches.

It is February. The oak has been dead a year.
I remember the great sails of its branches
rolling out greenly, a hundred and twenty feet up,
and acorns thick on the lawn.
Nine cities of squirrels lived in that tree.
Today they run over the snow
squeaking their lamentation.

Yet I was happy that it was coming down.
"Let it come down!" I kept saying to myself
with a joy that was strange to me.
Though the oak was the shade of old summers,
I loved the guttural saw.

Donald Hall

Twin Lakes Hunter

Last night a freezing cottontail
Slept just outside our outside door
And drew upon the heat that leaked
Through threshold from the floor.

Rex, the hunter told me so.
"Cold out," he said. "Some storm!"
He hoped the little fellow
Slept snug enough and warm.

He backed up to the Monarch range,
A-shiver in his mackinaw.
"I been outside an hour," he said.
"Take me a week to thaw."

"Snug, so you can shoot him later?"
He answered, "Please don't scold.
It's just I can't abide the thought
Of dying from the cold."

A. B. Guthrie, Jr.

Dreams

Hold fast to dreams
For if dreams die
Life is a broken-winged bird
That cannot fly.

Hold fast to dreams
For when dreams go
Life is a barren field
Frozen with snow.

              Langston Hughes

Legacy

The year has made her will: she left to me
A private purse:
Silver and copper from the dogwood tree,
White gold from a torrent, amber from a pond
And, for my sadness' sake,
Mountains in a bluescape of beyond.
It might be worse:
These will be useful when I lie awake.

Christopher Morley

A Patch of Old Snow

There's a patch of old snow in a corner
That I should have guessed
Was a blow-away paper the rain
Had brought to rest.

It is speckled with grime as if
Small print overspread it,
The news of a day I've forgotten—
If I ever read it.

Robert Frost

Preparation

Last fall I saw the farmer follow
The plow that dug the long dark furrows
Between the hillslope and the hollow.

All winter long the land lay fallow.
The woodchuck slept within his burrow
And heard no hound or farm boy's hallow.

Tonight the rain drives its dark arrows
Deep in the soil, down to its marrow.
The arrows of the sun tomorrow.

Robert Francis

Leathery, wry, and rough,
Jaw full of chaw, and slits
For eyes—this guy is tough.
He climbs the slatted fence,
Pulls himself atop and sits;
Tilts back his cowboy hat,
Stained with sweat below
The crown, and wipes a dirty
Sleeve across his brow;
Then pulls the hat down tight,
Caresses up its sides,
And spits into the dust
A benediction.

Gracelessly, his Brahma bull
Lunges into the chute
And swings a baleful
Eye around, irresolute.

Vision narrower still,
The man regards the beast.
There's weight enough to kill,
Bone and muscle fit at least
To jar a man apart.
The cowboy sniffs and hitches at
His pants. Himself all heart
And gristle, he watches as
The hands outside the chute
Prepare the sacrificial act.
Standing now, and nerving up,
He takes his final measure
Of the creature's awful back.

Then he moves. Swerving up
And into place, he pricks
The Brahma's bullish pride.

The gate swings free, and
Screams begin to sanctify
Their pitching, tortured ride.

Rodeo By Edward Lueders

Reflections on a Gift

of Watermelon Pickle

Received from a Friend

Called Felicity

During that summer
When unicorns were still possible;
When the purpose of knees
Was to be skinned;
When shiny horse chestnuts
  (Hollowed out
  Fitted with straws
  Crammed with tobacco
  Stolen from butts
  In family ashtrays)
Were puffed in green lizard silence
While straddling thick branches
Far above and away
From the softening effects
Of civilization;

During that summer—
Which may never have been at all;
But which has become more real
Than the one that was—
Watermelons ruled.

Thick pink imperial slices
Melting frigidly on sun-parched tongues
Dribbling from chins;
Leaving the best part,
The black bullet seeds,
To be spit out in rapid fire
Against the wall
Against the wind
Against each other;

And when the ammunition was spent,
There was always another bite:
It was a summer of limitless bites,
Of hungers quickly felt
And quickly forgotten
With the next careless gorging.

The bites are fewer now.
Each one is savored lingeringly,
Swallowed reluctantly.

But in a jar put up by Felicity,
The summer which maybe never was
Has been captured and preserved.
And when we unscrew the lid
And slice off a piece
And let it linger on our tongue:
Unicorns become possible again.

John Tobias

INTERPRETATION

UNFOLDING BUD (page 17)
How is the poem at "a first glance" like the tiny bud? According to the first stanza, what happens to a water-lily bud with each passing day? What makes a poem unfold? How are the bud and the poem alike after they have unfolded?

Which can live longer, a water-lily blossom or a good poem?

GONE FOREVER (page 18)
The first part of "Gone Forever" deals with writing a poem. The speaker in this poem, the "I," is a poet. What came to the poet as he was shaving? What happened to it?

This experience reminds the poet of other things that are "gone forever." What are they?

POETS HITCHHIKING ON THE HIGHWAY (page 19)
What kind of war are the poets having? Does either win?

TO LOOK AT ANY THING (page 21)
What might this poem suggest about reading a poem? About writing a poem? About understanding any thing?

ABSOLUTES (page 23)
How many things besides "black on white" suggest winter?

In an ink painting, everything is black and white. In the poem, another color is suggested. What is it? What word suggests it?

Does the shape of the poem look like what the poem is about?

THE CROWS (page 24)
The opening four lines of this poem set the scene and introduce the characters. Notice that the details are crowded together and that the

poem is happening *right now*. What is the setting? Who is Wade? What are his "tipsy shocks"? Who is "this form" in line 3, and what is "it" doing?

What words tell you whether the speaker likes the crows?

CROWS (page 25)
Which of the stanzas in this poem suggest sound? Movement?

Find examples in the poem of crows doing things people do.

SOME BROWN SPARROWS (page 27)
What advantage do the sparrows have over the creatures they visit?

What advantages, not stated in the poem, might the zoo creatures have over the sparrows? What might the poem suggest about *people?*

SWALLOWS (page 27)
What words in the first four lines indicate where the action takes place?

In the last four lines are the swallows winning their struggle with the wind?

SEAL (page 29)
Both the photograph and the poem present a seal in a true or accurate way. What do you learn about the seal from the poem that you cannot learn from the photograph?

Find examples of color, motion, and sound in the poem. Which is used most?

BOY WITH FROGS (page 30)
At the beginning of the poem, what has the boy just done? In the following three stanzas, what does the boy do with the frogs? What is his attitude toward them?

In what ways is the boy like a god to the frogs?

GIRAFFES (page 31)

One meaning of the first word, "stilted," is *stiffly dignified.* What other meaning of "stilted" applies to giraffes?

"Long-pronged legs" suggests the giraffes' height. What other phrases suggest the same thing?

"Bizarre" means *odd, strange,* or *fantastic.* What phrases in the poem show the giraffe to be "bizarre"?

WHY NOBODY PETS THE LION AT THE ZOO (page 33)

What do the first two lines say about the way men and lions have always gotten along?

What was the speaker taught about the lion's right to bite? Does the speaker think this teaching was right or wrong?

According to the poem, why is it that nobody pets the lion at the zoo?

THE BAT (page 34)

If you were to consult an encyclopedia about bats, you might find statements like these:

> A bat is a flying mammal. The mother bat usually bears one baby in the spring. She carries her baby with her for several weeks, then hangs it up. Bats usually rest during the day, hanging upside down. They hibernate in cold weather. Most bats feed chiefly on insects.

What similar facts can you find in the poem? What important additional impression about the bat do you get from the poem?

Who is speaking in the encyclopedia article? Who is speaking (who is the "I") in the poem?

THE BAT (page 35)

Where does the bat like to spend the day?

What lines in the poem describe how a bat behaves at night?

In what ways are bats like mice? Like birds? Like people? Which comparison seems most frightening?

DEER HUNT (page 36)

What is the usual hunting season? During what season is the hunting in this poem taking place? How is this possible?

In what ways is the speaker, the "I" in the poem, *not* like the other hunters? What made him join the hunters?

STEAM SHOVEL and THE TOASTER (page 37)

What part of this poem tells directly what the dinosaur is? What parts of the steam shovel are like what parts of the dinosaur? What does the steam shovel do that a dinosaur might do?

Which do you think provides the better comparison, the toaster-dragon or the steam shovel-dinosaur?

ON WATCHING THE CONSTRUCTION OF A SKYSCRAPER (page 38)

Poems are filled with **images** (or word pictures) that appeal to the senses of sight, sound, taste, touch, and smell. To what senses do the images in this poem appeal chiefly? Do any words in this poem appeal to the sense of smell?

Read the first line aloud stressing *orange* rather than *trees*. Then stress *trees* rather than *orange*. The image of the orange trees suggests both a natural tree and a steel framework painted with a coat of rust-proofing. What words can you find to support both images?

APARTMENT HOUSE (page 39)

To what two things is an apartment house compared? What do you think is the attitude of the speaker toward apartment houses?

THE BUILDERS (page 40)

Read this poem several times, first silently and then aloud.

In the fable of the three pigs, the first two are eaten by the wolf and the third survives. In this poem what did the third pig expect the other two pigs to do when the wolf came? Under what conditions would he have been "willing to help them"? What does he really care about?

TRANSCONTINENT (page 41)
What do the first two stanzas describe? To where does the scene shift in stanza three? What signals the end of the journey?

ADVICE TO TRAVELERS (page 42)
This is a poem with a lesson, or moral. What is the moral? What, other than a place, might "where you're going" mean?

CROSSING (page 43)
Some poems tell *about* an experience. Others try to present the experience as if it is happening now. Which does "Crossing" do?

What experience should the reader have had in order to appreciate the sound of this poem? Say aloud slowly, "Anaconda, Hiawatha, Lackawanna." Repeat the three words several times, building speed as you do. What does the sound suggest?

CROSSING KANSAS BY TRAIN (page 45)
In what direction do you think the train is traveling? Tell what the speaker sees.

AFRICAN SUNRISE (page 46)
What details suggest the location of this poem? To what are the winds compared? To what does "yellow" in line 4 refer?

Images, you remember, appeal to the physical senses. Find at least two images that appeal to the sense of sight. Find at least one image that appeals to the sense of touch, one to sound, and one to smell.

How are "hours" like a "caravan" in the line "the caravan of hours"?

CENTRAL PARK TOURNEY (page 47)
Central Park is in New York City. Through it, day and night, passes much of the city's traffic. What kind of contest seems to be going on in the traffic? Which lines, in particular, explain the title?

To which sense do the images in this poem have most appeal?

AUGUST FROM MY DESK (page 49)

Where is the speaker writing from? What does the heat remind him of?

What, in particular, does the speaker remember about his boyhood? What was the occupation of his father? What one word suggests a basic difference between father and son?

Did the speaker get what he dreamed about as a boy? How do you know?

KANSAS BOY (page 50)

In what ways is the "sea" described in this poem similar to a real ocean?

Which two lines in the poem describe an ancestor of the boy? Where was this ancestor from? What did he do for a living? What influence does this ancestor have on the boy?

WONDER WANDER (page 51)

The order of this poem follows the speaker's impressions as he wanders and watches. What impressions do you get about the speaker?

What might be the poet's reason for omitting punctuation and capitalization?

REFLECTIONS DENTAL (page 52)

Teeth are called "teeth" in line 2. Find three terms that substitute for "teeth" later on in the poem. Which seems to you the most descriptive?

For fourteen lines the poet describes the "beautiful," "fine" teeth of television performers. What unexpected attitude toward these teeth do you find in the two final lines of the poem?

One characteristic of poetry is that it says things in fewer words than prose. This is called **compression.** The two final lines of this poem show how compression works. How might these lines be written in prose?

THE MICROSCOPE *(page 53)*

What was Anton doing that caused the townsfolk to fume and fuss?

Why do you suppose the "simple water drop" is "best of all" the things Anton saw under his microscope? Does the poem itself tell you?

CHILD ON TOP OF A GREENHOUSE *(page 54)*

What do you think "everyone" is shouting?

The wind adds a feeling of motion to the scene described in this poem. Find the three lines where the wind is involved, and name the things it is affecting.

LONELINESS *(page 55)*

What lines suggest that the speaker is younger than the "he" in this poem?

In the first two stanzas, how does the speaker feel toward the other person? How does the speaker's attitude change during the poem?

INDIANS *(page 57)*

List some of the specific things the speaker thinks about when Margaret mentions Indians. Add as many items as you can to his list.

ARITHMETIC *(page 58)*

Six of the nine sentences in this poem begin with the word "Arithmetic." Which of these six sentences do you think best tells what arithmetic is? The other three sentences begin with "If you." Do these also tell you something about arithmetic? Which one of the three seems most completely a "fun" sentence?

Practice reading the second "If you" sentence aloud. Do you think it should be read fast or slowly?

What do you think is the author's attitude toward arithmetic?

Try writing a poem of your own on another subject such as science, health, or grammar.

HUSBANDS AND WIVES (page 59)
People sometimes say the opposite of what they really mean in order to make a point more emphatic or sometimes just to be funny. This way of expressing an idea is called using **irony** or being ironical. What lines are ironic in this poem?

THIS IS JUST TO SAY (page 60)
What are the images in this poem? Which are most appealing in your judgment? To what sense or senses do they appeal?

THE NE'ER-DO-WELL (page 61)
What is Enoch's way of life? How does the banker regard Enoch's way of life? What line tells you?

MEDITATIO (page 61)
What habits of dogs make man appear to be superior? What "curious habits" of man do you think might make dogs appear superior?

SUMMONS (page 62)
To whom do you think the speaker is talking? Would you say the person spoken to is *more* observant of the world around him than the speaker, or is he *less* observant? Why does the speaker want this person to keep him from sleeping?

In what other ways is a person either "asleep" or "awake"?

ANCIENT HISTORY (page 63)
How does the speaker feel about ancient history? What do you think he means in the last two lines?

ON THE VANITY OF EARTHLY GREATNESS (page 63)
What kind of poem does the title lead you to expect? What kind of poem does it turn out to be? Each stanza begins with something grand, powerful, or famous. How does each end?

Is there a lesson in this poem? If so, what is it?

DUST (page 64)

In "Husbands and Wives" (page 59) you learned that when someone *says* the opposite of what he really thinks or means, he is using irony or being ironical. Another kind of irony also carries the idea of opposite. When something *happens* that is the opposite of what would naturally be expected to happen, the happening is ironical. Often an ironical situation is humorous in an unhappy or bitter way.

The author of this poem sets up an ironical situation. What stanza makes this an ironical poem?

REBECCA (page 65)

This poem is from a book called CAUTIONARY VERSES. If this poem is typical, what subjects might the other poems deal with?

Do you think the author *mainly* wants to warn people, or does he mainly want to make them laugh?

BONES (page 66)

In your opinion, which was worse: the pain or the cure?

OVERHEARD ON A SALTMARSH (page 67)

Read this strange conversation between a goblin and a nymph as though it were a fairy tale. Don't expect reality.

Read the poem aloud, trying to identify the goblin and the nymph by the way they would say their lines.

In fairy tales goblins and nymphs are spirits found in nature. Which one seems more a part of the saltmarsh itself? Why?

RÉSUMÉ (page 68)

What do you think is the speaker's attitude toward individuals of the kind addressed in "Résumé"?

A *résumé* is a kind of summing-up. To *resume* is to start again, to continue where you left off. How are both meanings involved in this poem?

LOST (page 69)

What human qualities are given to the boat? What human characteristics does the harbor have? To what is the boat compared?

FIFTEEN (page 70)

Find the places in the poem where the speaker talks about the motorcycle as though it were living.

In stanza three, what is the speaker considering doing? In stanza four, what *does* he do?

INTERLUDE III (page 71)

What caused the speaker to notice the insect he had crushed?

What word in stanza two, line 2, describes the "thing" the speaker was writing when he killed the insect? In this same stanza, does the speaker indicate that he, or nature, is the greater artist?

WAR (page 71)

What is the main image or picture given? What comparisons are suggested? Explain how this image demonstrates the horror of war.

TOO BLUE (page 73)

The kind of music originated by the American Negro called "the blues" was one way to express the sadness which is a part of everyone's life. In some ways this poem is like a blues song. Is the speaker really considering suicide? Quote lines from the poem to support your answer.

from TWO JAZZ POEMS (page 74)

Describe the speaker's appearance. What slang words does he use? What do you think they contribute to this poem?

Where in the poem do you learn the speaker's attitude toward his own music? What kind of person do you think has "ears to hear" this kind of music?

A CONEY ISLAND LIFE (page 74)

The speaker in this poem compares his life to experiences in the Coney Island amusement park. What specific comparisons does he make? What are the "helium hopes" that "break skyward"?

The old-style carousel, or merry-go-round, had a brass ring hanging just beyond the normal reach of the riders. Each time around, the rider would reach out, trying to catch the ring. If he could catch it, he would win a prize. Has the speaker caught his "brass-ring-sun" yet? What, in his life, might the "brass-ring-sun" be?

To what do you think "the game" refers, in the last line?

CARMEL POINT (page 75)

What is a "sea anemone" (ə nem'ə ni)? In stanzas two and three, to what is the anemone compared?

To which two of the five senses do most of the images appeal?

The last stanza breaks the silent spell of the slow undersea drama and gives the speaker's reaction to it. What is the speaker's reaction?

FORGIVE MY GUILT (page 76)

What colors would you expect to find in a story about birds wounded by a gun blast and swimming out to sea? What specific colors *do* you find in the picture given by the speaker? Why do you suppose the speaker has used the colors of precious metals to refer to the birds?

This poem can be divided into three parts: an introduction, the central incident, and a conclusion. Where does each part begin?

THE TERM (page 77)

How is the brown paper like a man? How is it unlike a man? Is the paper really "as it was before"?

SONIC BOOM (page 79)

The speaker in this poem begins by talking about sonic booms. What would cause the "pop" in the next-to-last line? What is the speaker's attitude toward what may happen to the world?

HEY DIDDLE DIDDLE and *LITTLE MISS MUFFET* (page 80)
A parody is a piece of writing that imitates another in such a way as to make fun of it. These two poems are parodies.

Write out the original "Hey Diddle Diddle" and compare it with the parody. What is the point of the parody? Which of the two poems, the original or the parody, is easier to understand? Why?

What two meanings are suggested in the final line of "Little Miss Muffet"?

EARTH (page 81)
How are the details beginning with "Ants" and ending with "maggots" alike? In which lines do you find the suggestion that there may be life on other planets?

If you remember this poem the next time you see a shooting star, what will be your thought?

EARTH (page 81)
What is ironic in the last two lines of the poem? (See page 143 for a discussion of irony.)

SOUTHBOUND ON THE FREEWAY (page 82)
What "creatures" has the speaker seen that he mistakes for earth people? Exactly what are the "transparent parts" and the "guts" in the third stanza? What are the "round feet" that "roll" and what are the "diagrams" or "measuring tapes" in stanzas four and five? What is the "five-eyed" creature with the turning "red eye" in stanza six?

What are the "soft shapes, shadowy inside"? What are they called in line 4? What question is raised in the last line? Does this poem compliment man or criticize him? Explain.

FUELED (page 83)
To what is the launching of a rocket compared? In what ways are the two launchings similar? In what ways are they very different?

What change in man does this poem suggest would be desirable?

UNSATISFIED YEARNING (page 85)

What is unusual about the word arrangement in line 2? Read it aloud as you would ordinarily find it. What feeling does the arrangement in the poem give?

"In order to" can have two meanings in this poem. What are they?

PUPPY (page 86)

To whom is the speaker talking in the first stanza? What phrases suggest that the puppy is ferocious? Afraid? Crafty?

In the second stanza, with whose eyes is the speaker seeing the world? (Note the appropriateness of the description of the sun.)

SUNNING (page 86)

This poem is a kind of moving picture. What are some other details you could add that would continue the development of its mood or feeling?

ELEGY FOR JOG (page 87)

The dictionary states that an elegy is a *mournful or melancholy poem; poem that is a lament for the dead.* To what extent is the title appropriate or "right" for this poem?

If the dog is already dead, where is the "curb" in line 2? Who is now the dog's master? Where is the "traffic's hedge" that opens to let him in? What advice for human beings is contained in the last two lines?

CATALOGUE (page 89)

In what two ways does the title fit the poem? Read "Catalogue" aloud. What lines, in your opinion, best describe a cat? What cat sounds are described?

POEM (page 90)

This poem tries in the simplest and most direct way possible to make us *see* the movement of the cat as it goes through one particular action—with nothing extra. In fact, part of this poem isn't written at all. For instance, what might you be hearing and seeing *after* the last stanza?

Try writing a one sentence (not one line) poem about some animal other than a cat. Consider how the poem should look on the page. Consider, too, whether each word is the best you can find for the animal you are describing.

ON A NIGHT OF SNOW (page 91)
Who is the speaker in the first eight lines of this poem? What feeling toward the cat is expressed?

Who is the speaker in the last six lines? What quality of the cat is expressed? What differences are there in the attitudes of the two speakers toward the "wild winds" blowing outside?

FOR A DEAD KITTEN (page 92)
Why is the last word in the poem capitalized?

In what ways is "For a Dead Kitten" like "Elegy for Jog," page 87?

OZ. (page 93)
How do you pronounce the title of this poem?

What two "ounces" is the speaker referring to in the first stanza? How is the jungle ounce like a house cat? How is it different? What words are particularly good descriptions of any cat?

Which is most obvious in this poem—irony, sound, or compression?

APRIL (page 95)
What is the "it" in this poem?

Which images in the poem appeal to the sense of taste? Find the images that suggest water in some form. What connection has water with April?

In the last two lines, what is the boy selling?

IN JUST- (page 96)

Cummings uses typography (printed letters) to help illustrate or suggest the thing, or sight, or sound that he is writing about. Why do you think he put extra spaces between the words in line 5? What reason can you think of for writing "eddieandbill" and "bettyandisbel" as one word.

If you have studied Greek mythology, you may remember Pan, a god who had the legs of a goat and played on musical pipes. In what ways does the balloonman resemble Pan?

THE CHILD'S MORNING (page 97)

What time of year is this poem concerned with? Which details could apply equally well to another season? What one item controls or affects the images in the first eight lines?

What two senses does the line "Under surf of rollerskates" appeal to? Find other individual lines which appeal to more than one sense.

FOUR LITTLE FOXES (page 98)

What things do you *know* about the speaker in this poem? What things can you guess about him? Whom does the speaker address?

Why must the reader read lines 1 and 4 of each stanza differently from lines 2 and 3?

What happened to the mother fox? Does the poem tell whether the speaker was able to save the foxes?

FOUR DUCKS ON A POND (page 99)

To what sense do the images in the first four lines appeal? Only one image clearly suggests motion. Which one? What line controls or changes the mood of the poem?

COUNTING-OUT RHYME (page 99)

What does this poem talk about? Practice reading each stanza aloud as fast as you can and still be understood. What do you think the poet most wanted you to enjoy about it?

APRIL (page 99)

How does the poet want the reader to feel about the little goat? What qualities does the goat have? Why might he suddenly leap into the air?

What two meanings does the word *spring* have?

SWIFT THINGS ARE BEAUTIFUL (page 101)

What swift things are listed? What slow things? Which of the two verses seems to move more quickly as it is read aloud?

Do the beautiful things listed in the poem come from nature or from man-made sources?

Find another pair of opposites (for example, tall things and short) for a new list of your own. Polish your list and write it as a poem.

FORTUNE (page 102)

How old do you think the speaker and Molly were when all this happened? How old do you think the speaker is now?

What was the "fortune cookie" that the speaker is recalling? What is his attitude toward the incident? Why do you think he capitalized "FIREMEN"?

Does the speaker remember the incident clearly? How do you know?

This poem has an unusual arrangement on the page. Try reading the poem aloud so that your reading fits the poet's arrangement.

FISH STORY (page 104)

What, in your own words, is one of the speaker's wishes? Which two lines of the fish's story are most typical of a fisherman's story?

ANGLER'S CHOICE (page 105)

What is the last fishing lure tried by the speaker in the poem? How is it different from all the others?

The poet has used the names of fishing flies to help him make a poem. Poetic words from other sports might include: fireballer, squeeze play, line drive, flying tackle, lonesome end, clipping, and goal-line stand. These words suggest mental pictures. Think of other sports (or non-sport activities, such as coin collecting) that have terms a poet might use. Make a short poem from your list.

THE FISHER (page 105)

Where is "the tune" in line 3 being played and by whom? The fisher-man is not going fishing at four-thirty just to catch fish. What other reason does the poem suggest?

Which images in this poem appeal to the sense of hearing? Find phrases which appeal to the sense of touch.

HUNTING SONG (page 106)

How are the four stanzas of this poem alike? What part of the hunt does each of the stanzas picture? Why couldn't the order of these stanzas be changed?

How is the fox's view of the hunt different from the views of the hounds and the hunter?

The poet gives the log the qualities of a living thing. How does the log's view of the hunt differ from the other three? In what way does the log watch death go "through him, Around him, and over him"? Does the poem actually state that the fox was killed? How do you know that he was?

THE TRAP (page 108)

Do you think the old man in this poem is cruel? What do you think is his *real* reason, near the end of the poem, for deciding to "ride into the back field, first thing"?

Why does the wife smile "almost secretly to herself"?

FIREWORKS (page 109)

Describe the sound with which the fireworks display begins. How many sets of fireworks does the poem describe? To what flowers are they compared? Read the lines that show how each set disappears.

THE GARDEN HOSE (page 110)
What two lines bring the image of the garden hose to life?

LULLABY (page 111)
Why would this poem be less effective as a lullaby if the boat were a rowboat instead of a canoe?

What does the refrain "One . . . two . . . / Three . . . four. . . ." refer to? What sounds are suggested in the poem?

THE BASE STEALER (page 112)
What baseball situation is described in the poem? What tells you? To what four things is the base runner compared?

How does the poet build up a feeling of suspense? What do you think happened in the last line? Do you think the runner is "out" or "safe"? Does the poem tell you in any way?

FOUL SHOT (page 112)
What is the setting for this poem? What is the score?

Compare this poem with "The Base Stealer." How are they alike? What do the one-word lines add to this poem?

MILLIONS OF STRAWBERRIES (page 114)
In the first line, what is the "curve"? About what time of day is it at the beginning of the poem? What line tells you? About what time is it at the end of the poem? What two lines tell you?

CHEERS (page 115)
Read this poem aloud. How are the sounds in the two stanzas different? If the frog and the snake were not mentioned by name in the last two stanzas, how would you know which one was cheering?

Sisyphus, Scylla, and Charybdis are characters or things found in mythology. Why do you think the snake would be more apt to use words from mythology than the frog?

THE FORECAST (page 117)
Is "the forecast" in this poem in the newspaper or on television? What have we lost from our lives that has been replaced by "the forecast"?

What is the attitude of the speaker in the poem toward the times we live in?

MOTHER'S BISCUITS (page 118)
What time of year does the speaker associate with memories of the biscuits? What are the "kitchen-nights" referred to in the second stanza?

TWO LIVES AND OTHERS (page 119)
Although the season of the year is revealed in many details in this poem, you are not *told* what time of year it is until the last line. What are the first two details that give clues to the season?

Which of the images in the poem suggest *cold?* What images could be from any time of year?

THE PHEASANT (page 120)
What words in the first six lines describe the pheasant's attitude? After the bird is shot, how does this attitude change?

NOVEMBER DAY (page 121)
In what way are autumn trees like pheasants? What do "her" and "she" refer to in lines 4 and 5? What are being hung "In rows"? What does the "brilliant plumage" in line 7 refer to?

GREY GOOSE (page 122)
This poem is the lyric, or words, from a folk song. Folk songs and ballads are created over the years (and only sometimes written down) by unknown singers. Folk singers often change the lines around to suit themselves as time goes on, sometimes even add verses of their own. Basic interests and hopes and fears often make up the subjects

of folk music. What is the subject of this song? How do you think the singer of it would want you to react?

WILD GOOSE (page 123)

What is the general setting of the poem? Cite lines that tell you.

According to the speaker, are geese silly?

FALL (page 123)

Ducks and geese flying south are a familiar **symbol** or sign of fall. What line expresses this symbol in a particularly fresh manner?

VALENTINE (page 124)

The first stanza begins like a nonsense verse but concludes with two more meaningful lines. Does this pattern continue through all three stanzas? How do you think the poet wants you to respond to this?

OREGON WINTER (page 125)

Is the winter described here different from the winter you know? In what ways?

What contrasts are included in the poem? What individual pictures do you think are most effective?

THE STUMP (page 126)

Poets use many symbols. Geese flying south can be symbols of approaching winter; hearts symbolize love; cats can be symbols of mystery; lemonade and daisies can be symbols of April. In this poem the oak tree is, on a literal level, simply an oak tree. It has died and is being cut down. But as you read the poem, you become aware that it means more to the speaker in the poem than would first appear.

With what did the speaker associate the oak tree? Why might he be strangely happy it was coming down?

What symbolizes the present? Does the speaker find this desirable or undesirable?

TWIN LAKES HUNTER (page 127)

How many people speak in this poem? Is the person who says, "Snug, so you can shoot him later?" a man or a woman? What word in the poem gives you a clue?

What have Rex and the rabbit in common? Why might Rex be willing to shoot the rabbit yet not want it to die from the cold?

DREAMS (page 129)

Life is compared with what two things? Which do you think is the richer, more revealing comparison?

LEGACY (page 130)

With what is "The year" compared? What treasure was left to the speaker? Is the person who receives the treasure delighted with it or does he seem merely willing to accept it?

A PATCH OF OLD SNOW (page 130)

What, for a moment, does the speaker think the snow is? What relation has the second stanza to his mistaken idea? In stanza two, what is the "it" of the first line? The "it" of the second line? The "it" of line 4?

PREPARATION (page 131)

What season does stanza one deal with? What season does stanza two deal with? What time of year is the "Tonight" of stanza three? What does "the sun tomorrow" represent?

After reading the poem, what do you think the title means?

RODEO (page 133)

Which do you think tells a more detailed story, the poem or the picture?

What details does the picture give that are not mentioned in the poem? What details does the poem give you that the picture does not?

REFLECTIONS ON A GIFT OF WATERMELON PICKLE RECEIVED FROM A FRIEND CALLED FELICITY (page 134)
A unicorn is an imaginary beast, so-called because one (*uni*) horn (*corn*) protruded from its forehead. What time of one's life is the time when "unicorns" are "still possible"?

What does the speaker suggest in the line "Which may never have been at all"? About how old do you think the speaker is now?

Why is the word "imperial" a particularly good word to describe the slices of watermelon? (In this connection, reread the preceding line.)

How do the "bites" taken now differ from those taken earlier? What kinds of experiences does the watermelon now symbolize?

What effect does the gift from Felicity have on the speaker?

AUTHOR-TITLE INDEX